The Pittsburgh SPORTS WIZ Trivia QUIZ

by Harry Patterson

RED-LETTER PRESS, INC.

THE PITTSBURGH SPORTS WIZ TRIVIA QUIZ
Copyright ©2000 Red-Letter Press, Inc.
ISBN: 0-940462-89-3
All Rights Reserved
Printed in the United States of America

For information address:

Red-Letter Press, Inc.
P.O. Box 393, Saddle River, NJ 07458

ABOUT THE AUTHOR

Harry Patterson is a free-lance writer, bartender, trivia maven and lifelong Pittsburgh resident. He attended Fox Chapel High School, Community College of Allegheny County, the University of Pittsburgh and served in the U.S. Army. This is the first of a series of sports-related books Mr. Patterson is writing for Red-Letter Press.

DEDICATED TO: Ma

SPECIAL THANKS TO:

Bill Brown
George Couples
Peggy Dimperio
Jack McVay
Bill Moushey
Tom O'Malley Jr.
Bill Rodgers
Mike Ryan
Keith Wehner
The staff at the Shaler North Hills Library
The gang at the River City Inn

ACKNOWLEDGMENTS

Cover design
and typography: s.w.artz, inc.

Editorial: Ellen Fischbein

Contributors: Angela Demers,
Mike Ryan
and Jim Tomlinson

INTRODUCTION

Red-Letter Press proudly steps up to the plate with *The Pittsburgh Sports Wiz Trivia Quiz.* Formatted in ten-question quizzes, it features an all-star selection of stumpers on the Steel City's sports scene.

Harry Patterson brings you a book loaded with local trivia … Which member of the Four Horsemen of Notre Dame later coached at Duquesne? … What Dallas Cowboy shared the cover of *Newsweek* with Terry Bradshaw prior to Super Bowl XIII? … Before Willie Stargell came along, which Bucco held the all-time single season record for homers by a first baseman?*

Now let's find out if you're a Pittsburgh sports nut or not. Let the quizzes begin.

Jack Kreismer
Publisher

*The answers are: Elmer Layden, Thomas "Hollywood" Henderson and Dr. Strangeglove, Dick Stuart (35 in 1961).

First of All

1. Who was the very first Dapper Dan Man of the Year?
2. Who scored the very first Pittsburgh Penguins goal?
3. Which former Pirate became the first pitcher to be used as a designated hitter?
4. On October 13, 1971 the Pirates hosted the first night game in World Series history. Who was the winning pitcher?
5. Who was the Pirates starting pitcher that night?
6. Babe Ruth's final career home run, hit in 1935 at Forbes Field, was also the first homer to do what?
7. Who hit the first (and only) homer over the deepest part of the center field wall (457 feet) at Forbes Field?
8. The Pirates lost the first night home opener in major league history to the Cardinals in St. Louis. What was the year?
9. In what year was the Pirates first night home opener?
10. Which Pirate hit the first home run in World Series history?

Sec. 82 | Row E | Seat 17 | Enter Gate B

"I'd have to be up another solar system to be able to get on their wavelength."

-Kevin Stevens, when asked if he had some moves like Jaromir Jagr and Mario Lemieux

Answers

1. Billy Conn
2. Andy Bathgate
3. Rick Rhoden (for the Yankees)
4. The Pirates Bruce Kison
5. Luke Walker
6. It was the first of only 17 homers to clear the right field roof.
7. Dick Stuart in 1969
8. 1950
9. 1985
10. Jimmy Sebring

"I may be dumb, but I'm not stupid."

-Terry Bradshaw

Sec. 16

Row 51

Seat 7a

**Enter
Gate G**

Lower Tier

Deuces

1. At what two home facilities did the AHL Pittsburgh Hornets play?

2. Name the two Steelers coaches who came between Buddy Parker and Chuck Noll.

3. What were the nicknames of Pittsburgh's two Negro League baseball teams?

4. Name the two Pittsburgh pro basketball teams that Connie Hawkins played for.

5. Forbes Field was located at the corner of which two Oakland streets?

6. Who is the only Pirate to win two (BBWAA) MVP awards?

7. Which two Pirates pitchers pitched (as Pirates) for Danny Murtaugh, Chuck Tanner and Jim Leyland?

8. Name the only two Pirate Cy Young Award winners.

9. Name the only two Pitt basketball coaches in the seventies.

10. Respectively, who were "Big Poison" and "Little Poison"?

Answers

1. Duquesne Gardens and the Civic Arena
2. Mike Nixon and Bill Austin were a combined 13-40-3.
3. The Pittsburgh Crawfords and the Homestead Grays
4. The Rens (ABL) and the Pipers (ABA)
5. Bouquet and Sennott
6. Barry Bonds
7. Jerry Reuss and John Candelaria
8. Vernon Law (1960) and Doug Drabek (1990)
9. Buzz Ridl and Tim Grgurich
10. Paul and Lloyd Waner

FULL SEASON

Sec. 17
Row K
Seat 22
Gate F

"The way I've been going, I couldn't drive Miss Daisy home."

–Pirates outfielder Andy Van Slyke, on his RBI slump

Threes

1. Name the three rivers of Three Rivers Stadium.

2. George Blanda is the NFL's all-time leading scorer with 2002 total points (TDs, FGs, PATs). Which three players, who each spent part of his career with the Steelers, are in the top 15 all-time?

3. Name the three Pitt Panthers taken in the first round of the NFL draft in 1981.

4. There are three statues outside Three Rivers Stadium. Name the three Pittsburgh sports legends that they depict.

5. Three Rivers is one of three multi-purpose "cookie cutter" stadiums built in the early seventies. Where are the other two?

6. Pittsburgh is one of only three cities to have teams win both the Super Bowl and the Stanley Cup. What are the other two?

7. In which three sports, other than baseball, was there a local pro team known as the Pittsburgh Pirates?

8. Which Hall of Famer hit the final three homers of his career at Forbes Field as a member of the Boston Braves?

9. From the sixties to the nineties the position of Steelers center has been dominated by only three men. Who are they?

10. Only three shortstops have won National League batting titles in the 20th century. All were Pirates. Who were they?

Answers

1. The Allegheny, the Monongahela and the Ohio
2. Gary Anderson, Matt Bahr and Norm Johnson
3. Mark May, Hugh Green and Randy McMillan
4. Honus Wagner, Art Rooney and Roberto Clemente
5. Philadelphia and Cincinnati
6. Chicago (Bears, Blackhawks) and New York (Jets and Giants, Rangers and Islanders)
7. Football (the original name of the Steelers), hockey (an NHL team in the twenties) and basketball (a National Basketball League team in the thirties)
8. Babe Ruth
9. Ray Mansfield, Mike Webster and Dermontti Dawson
10. Honus Wagner, Arky Vaughan and Dick Groat

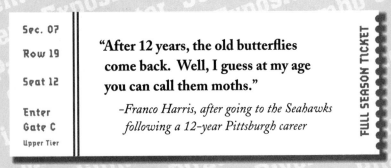

Sec. 07
Row 19
Seat 12

Enter
Gate C
Upper Tier

FULL SEASON TICKET

"After 12 years, the old butterflies come back. Well, I guess at my age you can call them moths."

–Franco Harris, after going to the Seahawks following a 12-year Pittsburgh career

Pittsburgh Potpourri

1. On June 18, 1941 the Pirates-Giants game at Forbes Field went into an extended, non-weather related delay. Why?

2. How many Calder Cups (AHL equivalent of the Stanley Cup) did the Pittsburgh Hornets win?

3. Who won an Olympic gold medal with the U.S. Women's Basketball Team in 1988 and went pro with the Cleveland Rockers in 1998?

4. Brothers Danny and Rick Seemiller of Carrick were top ranked in what sport in the seventies?

5. What former Pirate was Mark McGwire's hitting coach when he hit 70 homers?

6. What legendary Pittsburgh character was the "doorman" at the Pirates locker room after Maz's World Series homer?

7. How many City League championships did the legendary coach Pete Dimperio win in his 21 seasons at Westinghouse?

8. What local high school did Stan Musial pitch for?

9. Name the Duquesne basketball star who married actress-dancer Debbie Allen.

10. What was the ultimate accolade that a caller to Myron Cope's talk show could receive?

Answers

1. The radio broadcast of the first Joe Louis-Billy Conn bout was played over the PA. The Pirates lost, too.

2. Three, in 1952, 1955 and 1967

3. Suzie McConnell

4. Table tennis (or Ping-Pong)

5. Dave Parker

6. Joey Divin – Mayor Joe Barr and Bishop John Wright were among those he allowed to enter.

7. 17

8. Donora

9. Norm Nixon

10. To be dubbed a "Cope-a-nut" by Myron

Who Dat?

1. He was the narrator with the imposing voice so familiar to Steelers fans for his work for NFL films during the glory years ("the Pittsbugg Steeluhs").

2. This Pirates starting third baseman was lost to the 1998 expansion draft.

3. He was one of the best kickers in Pitt history, but in 1975 he missed three field goals and had an extra point blocked as Pitt lost, 7-6, to Penn State at Three Rivers Stadium.

4. A former Steeler (and Pitt Panther), he was instrumental in ending the 1982 football strike.

5. He served as head coach of the New York Jets, offensive coordinator of the Steelers and head football coach at Robert Morris.

6. He was head coach of the Arena Football Pittsburgh Gladiators as well as defensive coordinator for both the USFL Maulers and the NFL Atlanta Falcons.

7. The first black New York Yankee, he played against the Pirates in the 1960 World Series.

8. In 1946 (an 11 game season), he led the NFL in rushing yards (604) and interceptions (10). The latter is a club record that was tied a couple of times but stood until Mel Blount's 11 in 1975.

9. At age 35 he rushed for 1048 yards in a 12 game season becoming the oldest man to rush for 1000 yards until John Riggins in the eighties (in a 16 game season).

10. He was signed by the Steelers in 1938 for a then unheard of $15,000. In his one season with the team he led the NFL in rushing and was Rookie of the Year.

Answers

1. John Facenda
2. Joe Randa
3. Carson Long
4. Paul Martha
5. Joe Walton
6. Joe Haering
7. Elston Howard
8. "Bullet" Bill Dudley
9. John Henry Johnson
10. Byron "Whizzer" White

Sec. 82 Row E Seat 17

Enter Gate B

"It was a rash statement, and I'd like to apologize to every vulture in the sky."

—Pitt coach Mike Gottfried, on commenting that all sports agents are vultures

Gazing at the All-Stars I

1. The first Major League Baseball All-Star Game took place at Comiskey Park in Chicago on July 6, 1933. Connie Mack managed the American League team. John McGraw managed the National League team. Babe Ruth, Lou Gehrig and Jimmie Foxx were among the All-Stars. Which two players represented the Pirates? (Hint: Their last names rhyme.)

The All-Star Game has been played in Pittsburgh four times; twice at Forbes Field (1944 & 1959) and twice at Three Rivers (1974 & 1994). Which league won in:

2. 1944?

3. 1959?

4. 1974?

5. 1994?

6. The 1959 All-Star Game at Forbes Field was the first of two games played that year. This was the first of four consecutive years that two games were played. Why were two All-Star Games played during those years?

7. Name the four Pirates players on the 1959 National League All-Star team.

8. Name the Pirates sole representative on the 1974 National League All-Star team. (Hint: He was also the winning pitcher.)

9. Name the Pirates sole representative on the 1994 National League All-Star team.

10. Name the four ex-Bucs on the 1994 National League All-Star team.

Answers

1. Pie Traynor and Paul Waner

2 – 5. It was never a shame at the All-Star Game in Pittsburgh. The home team National League won all four times.

6. To help the players' pension fund

7. Smoky Burgess, Elroy Face, Dick Groat and Bill Mazeroski

8. Ken Brett

9. Carlos Garcia

10. Barry Bonds (Giants), Doug Drabek (Astros), Moises Alou (Expos) and Danny Jackson (Phillies)

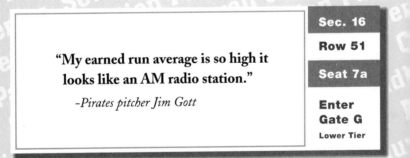

"My earned run average is so high it looks like an AM radio station."

–Pirates pitcher Jim Gott

Sec. 16

Row 51

Seat 7a

Enter
Gate G
Lower Tier

Steelers Stumpers

1. What was the original nickname of the Steelers?

2. What year did they first play under the name Steelers?

3. True or false? The Steelers once had cheerleaders known as the Steelerettes.

4. What defensive back (and current NFL head coach) once filled in as an emergency quarterback sub for the Steelers?

5. John Stallworth is first and Lynn Swann is third in Steelers all-time receiving yards. Who is second?

6. Which of the following was never a quarterback for the Steelers?

   Ted Marchibroda, Jack Kemp, Johnny Unitas, Len Dawson or Earl Morrall

7. The Steelers were the last NFL team to play the single wing. What year did they finally switch to the T-formation?

8. Who was the Steelers last regular season quarterback before Terry Bradshaw?

9. When Franco Harris became the Steelers all-time leading rusher, whose record did he surpass?

10. Until the Super Steelers of the seventies came along, who played the most seasons with the team?

Answers

1. The Pirates

2. 1941 – For the sake of consistency they will be referred to only as the Steelers from here on.

3. True – They came and went in 1968.

4. Tony Dungy

5. Louis Lipps

6. Unitas was drafted ninth by the Steelers, cut and claimed by the Colts.

7. 1952

8. Dick Shiner (1968-'69)

9. John Henry Johnson

10. Ernie Stautner, 14 seasons (1950-'63)

FULL SEASON

Sec. 17 Row K Seat 22 Gate F

"I just grab me an armful of men, pick 'em over until I find the one with the ball, then I throw him down."

–The self-described style of Steelers defensive lineman Gene "Big Daddy" Lipscomb

Buccos Brainteasers

1. What was the original nickname of the Pirates?

2. Bill Mazeroski holds the single season record for double plays (161 in 1966). Who was the Bucco shortstop that year?

3. Which member of the 1960 Pirates was grabbed by the Mets in the 1962 expansion draft?

4. Which Bucco was taken by the Expos in the 1968 expansion draft?

5. In what year was the first Pirates home night game?

6. Willie Stargell became the only player to hit a fair ball out of which park?

7. Stargell hit a single in his only at-bat in the last game of his career. What was his spot in the lineup that day?

8. Who was the last-ever pinch runner for Stargell?

9. Which Pirate hurler once won 17 straight decisions, finishing the season 18-1?

10. Can you think of the Buccos who have been named Rookie of the Year?

Answers

1. The Alleghenies
2. Gene Alley
3. Joe Christopher
4. Manny Mota
5. 1940 (against the Braves)
6. Dodger Stadium – He did it twice (in 1969 and 1974).
7. He batted first.
8. Doug Frobel
9. ElRoy Face (1959)
10. Probably not – there are none.

Sec. 07	"Just eliminating one discussion of the
Row 19	NFL draft on one sports talk show would
Seat 12	keep 500,000 pounds of hot air from
	being released into the atmosphere
Enter	and contributing to global warming."
Gate C	
Upper Tier	-Pittsburgh Post Gazette *writer Peter Leo*

FULL SEASON TICKET

By Any Other Name

The answers to the following are not generally known by their given first names which are provided in the clues.

1. Harry was a minority owner and vice-president of the Pirates. In his day job he was one of the most popular entertainers of the twentieth century.

2. Marvin sang the national anthem at the 1994 All-Star Game at Three Rivers Stadium.

3. Raymond made it to a single playoff game as coach of the Steelers, losing to Detroit, 17-10.

4. Harold was a former Pirates player and manager who threw out the first ball for game three of the 1971 World Series at Rivers Stadium.

5. Stephen came from Rochester, New York to attend Pitt and never left. His tavern/restaurant is often frequented by local and visiting sports figures.

6. Lawrence was the Yankees left fielder in game seven of the 1960 World Series who watched Maz's homer go over the wall.

7. Forrest spent over 15 seasons in the majors, including six as a Pirate. He appeared in over 500 games without fielding a defensive position (as well as over 1000 in which he did), but was never a DH.

8. Walter was the Steelers third round draft choice in 1986.

9. Hazen is a Pirates Hall of Famer who played on the 1925 World Champion team.

10. Robert finished his Steelers career with 3865 rushing yards, then fourth on the team's all-time list.

Answers

1. Bing Crosby
2. Meat Loaf
3. Buddy Parker
4. Pie Traynor
5. Froggy Morris
6. Yogi Berra
7. Smoky Burgess
8. Bubby Brister
9. Kiki Cuyler
10. Rocky Bleier

Sec. 82 Row E Seat 17 Enter Gate B

"You clowns can go on *What's My Line* in full uniforms and stump the panel."

–Manager Billy Meyer, addressing the pitiful Pirates of the early 1950s

There's a Draft in Here

1. Who was the Steelers first number one draft choice of the Chuck Noll era?

2. Who was the second round choice that same year?

3. Name the two future Hall of Famers chosen in Noll's second draft in 1970.

4. Name the two future Hall of Famers drafted by the Steelers out of Penn State in 1971 and 1972.

5. Name the two future Hall of Famers chosen in the 1974 Steelers draft.

6. What was the first year that a Chuck Noll draft did not include a future Hall of Famer?

7. Who was the only Pitt player to be a Steelers first round draft choice?

8. Who was the last quarterback taken in the first round by the Steelers?

9. Complete the following rhyming couplet about the 1956 Steelers draft:

    "Gary Glick, _____ _____ _____."

10. At the urging of broadcaster Myron Cope, the Steelers made this wrestling champ their final draft pick in 1989.

Answers

1. Joe Greene
2. Terry Hanratty
3. Terry Bradshaw (first) and Mel Blount (third)
4. Jack Ham (second in 1971) and Franco Harris (first in 1972)
5. Jack Lambert (second) and Mike Webster (fifth)
6. 1973 (though 1974 had two)
7. Paul Martha, 1964
8. Mark Malone, 1980
9. " . . . the Bonus Pick."
10. Carlton Haselrig

It's All Relative

1. Which DiMaggio brother played for the Pirates?

2. True or false? Jocelyn Lemieux, who was drafted by the Blues in 1986, is Mario's brother.

3. Though he never made it to the majors, for which organization did Roberto Clemente Jr. play?

4. Which organization signed his younger brother, Luis?

5. Which of hockey's Sutter brothers played for the Penguins?

6. Who were the twin basketball standouts from Fox Chapel High School who went on to excel at Duquesne?

7. Which one-time club pro at the Pittsburgh Field Club is the brother of one of golf's all-time greats?

8. True or false? Paul and Lloyd Waner are the only two brothers in the Hall of Fame.

9. True or false? Steelers running back and assistant coach Dick Hoak and the late Pirates third baseman Don Hoak were first cousins.

10. Former Pirates general manager Joe L. Brown is the son of which old-time comic?

Answers

1. Vince
2. False – He is the brother of Claude Lemieux.
3. The Philadelphia Phillies
4. The Pirates
5. Rich
6. Barry and Garry Nelson
7. Pete Snead, brother of Sam
8. True
9. False – They were not related.
10. Joe E. Brown

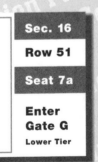

"When I was younger, yes."

-*Pirates manager Danny Murtaugh, when asked if he could have a better wish than Pittsburgh winning the World Series*

Sec. 16

Row 51

Seat 7a

**Enter
Gate G**

Lower Tier

Penguins Puzzlers

1. Who was the Pens first head coach?

2. Who was the first play-by-play man for the Pens?

3. Which Penguin was MVP of the 1973 All-Star Game?

4. Which Penguin was MVP of the 1975 All-Star Game?

5. What was Mike Lange's first season as the Pens play-by-play man?

6. Which Penguin became the first American-born NHL player to reach 1000 career points?

7. Who is the Pens all-time leader in minutes played?

8. Mario is second in games played with the Pens (745). Who's first?

9. Which Penguins coach has the most victories?

10. Which Penguins coach leads the team in all-time winning percentage?

FULL SEASON

Sec. 17
Row K
Seat 22
Gate F

"Some people have those games where you guess the number of people in the park. Here you have to identify them, too."

–Former outfielder Lee Mazzilli, on a small turnout at Three Rivers Stadium

Answers

1. Red Sullivan
2. Ed Conway
3. Greg Polis
4. Syl Apps
5. 1974-'75
6. Joe Mullen in 1995
7. Tom Barrasso
8. Jean Pronovost
9. Ed Johnston with 232
10. Scotty Bowman (.628)

Sec. 07

Row 19

Seat 12

Enter
Gate C
Upper Tier

FULL SEASON TICKET

"Given half the chance I'd punch one of them out. And it'd give me a lot of satisfaction."

–Mean Joe Greene, on NFL officials

Friendly Facilities

1. Who was the head groundskeeper at Three Rivers Stadium who tended to the field for six championship teams in the '70s?

2. Who was the longtime public address announcer for Pirates games at both Forbes Field and Three Rivers Stadium?

3. At which Pittsburgh venue was the closed circuit telecast of the first Ali-Frazier match on March 8, 1971 held?

4. When was the largest baseball crowd at Three Rivers Stadium?

5. When was the largest baseball crowd at Forbes Field?

6. What year did the Steelers string of consecutive sellouts at Three Rivers Stadium begin?

7. Only 13 homers (through 1998) have reached the upper deck at Three Rivers Stadium. Who hit five of them?

8. Eighteen homers were hit over the right field roof at Forbes Field. Who had seven of them?

9. Which Steelers division rival did not win a game at Three Rivers Stadium until 1986?

10. What distinction does Forbes Field hold regarding no-hitters?

Answers

1. Steve "Dirt" DiNardo

2. Art McKennan

3. Three Rivers Stadium – The Condors were playing at the Arena.

4. The 1994 All-Star Game (59,568)

5. Prize Day in 1956 vs. the Dodgers (44,932)

6. 1972 – November 5, 1972 against the Bengals to be precise

7. Willie Stargell

8. Willie Stargell

9. The Cleveland Browns

10. There was never a no-hitter pitched there.

"**Starting August 1, I don't order French fries with my club sandwich.**"

–Mario Lemieux, answering whether he worked out during the off-season

Hail to Pitt!

1. Who was the first Pitt football player to make it to the Pro Football Hall of Fame?

2. Which Pitt quarterback married the coach's daughter?

3. Pitt went 9-1 in 1963, losing only to Navy. Who was Navy's quarterback?

4. What mid-sixties Pitt linebacker later coached the Browns and the Chiefs in the NFL?

5. Who was Johnny Majors' first starting quarterback at Pitt?

6. What position did Rick Trocano move to at Pitt after losing the starting quarterback job to Dan Marino?

7. Which Pitt Panther won the Outland Trophy (best lineman) in 1980?

8. Who was Mike Ditka's coach at Pitt?

9. Who subbed for the injured Dan Marino when the Panthers beat West Virginia, 17-0, in 1981?

10. An upset Penn State victory ended a 17-game Pitt winning streak in 1981. Who was the Penn State quarterback?

Answers

1. Joe Schmidt – He played for the Detroit Lions.
2. Fred Mazurek married John Michelosen's daughter, Sue.
3. Roger Staubach
4. Marty Schottenheimer
5. Billy Daniels
6. Safety
7. Mark May
8. John Michelosen
9. Dan Daniels
10. Todd Blackledge

Hollywood
on the Rivers

1. In the 1995 movie *Sudden Death*, who did the Pens play in the fictional seventh game of the Stanley Cup finals at the Civic Arena?

2. Who played Rocky Bleier in *Fighting Back*, the TV movie of his autobiography?

3. Who played Steelers owner Art Rooney in *Fighting Back*?

4. What 1977 movie incorporated actual footage from Super Bowl X (Steelers vs. Cowboys) in its climax?

5. Name the future TV cop who played for the Vikings against the Steelers in Super Bowl IX.

6. Name the future TV cop who played for the Rams against the Steelers in Super Bowl XIV.

7. Name the three Burt Reynolds movies in which Terry Bradshaw had small parts.

8. What was the 1979 movie, filmed largely at the Civic Arena, about a fictional Pittsburgh pro basketball team?

9. Name the 1951 movie filmed in Pittsburgh that starred Paul Douglas as the manager of the hapless Pittsburgh Pirates and also featured Janet Leigh.

10. When the above movie was remade by Disney in 1994, at what facility was the world premiere held?

Answers

1. The Chicago Blackhawks
2. Robert Urich
3. Art Carney
4. *Black Sunday*
5. Running back Ed Marinaro – He later played Joe Coffey on *Hill Street Blues*.
6. Defensive lineman Fred Dryer – He later played Sgt. Rick Hunter on *Hunter*.
7. *Cannonball Run, Smokey and the Bandit II* and *Hooper*
8. *The Fish That Saved Pittsburgh*
9. *Angels in the Outfield*
10. At Three Rivers Stadium as part of the All-Star Game festivities

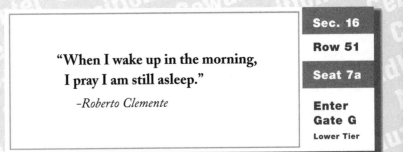

"When I wake up in the morning,
I pray I am still asleep."

–*Roberto Clemente*

Sec. 16

Row 51

Seat 7a

Enter
Gate G

Lower Tier

They Managed

1. Which Pirates manager did first base coach Danny Murtaugh replace after 103 games in 1957?

2. Murtaugh pulled four separate shifts as manager of the Pirates, a record until the Billy Martin circus in New York. Name the four managers who filled in the gaps between Murtaugh's goings and comings. (Hint: One was little more than a footnote.)

3. Name the next three Pirates managers after Murtaugh retired for the last time.

4. Which Pirates manager later became a head coach in the National Football League, and thus was the only man to serve as both a Major League Baseball manager and an NFL head coach?

5. True or false? Pirates legend Honus Wagner was also a Pirates manager.

6. Who is the only Pirates manager in the Hall of Fame as a manager?

7. Former Pirates center fielder and manager Bill Virdon later managed the New York Yankees. He is the only Yankees manager to never win a game at Yankee Stadium. Why?

8. Which team owner acted as his team's manager for a single game against the Pirates at Three Rivers Stadium?

9. Who is the only Buccos skipper to be named BBWAA National League Manager of the year?

10. Who is the only Pirates manager to win National League pennants with three different clubs?

Answers

1. Bobby Bragan
2. Harry Walker (1965-'67), Larry Shepard (1968-'69), Bill Virdon (1972-'73) and Alex Grammas who filled in at the end of 1969, going 4-1
3. Chuck Tanner, Jim Leyland and Gene Lamont
4. Hugo Bezdek – He managed the Pirates from 1917-'19 and coached the Cleveland Rams in 1937-'38.
5. True – He filled in at the end of his playing career in 1917, going 1-4.
6. Bill McKechnie (1922-'26) – He also managed in St. Louis, Boston and Cincinnati.
7. His stint took place while Yankee Stadium was undergoing extensive renovations and all home games were played at Shea Stadium.
8. The Atlanta Braves Ted Turner, on May 11, 1977 – He finished his managerial career with a record of 0-1.
9. Jim Leyland (in 1990 and 1992)
10. Bill McKechnie (1925 Pirates, 1928 Cardinals, 1930 and 1940 Reds)

Buccos on the Air

1. The very first live baseball broadcast was a Pirates home game on August 6, 1921 on KDKA radio. Who was the announcer for that game?

2. Who became the Pirates first full-time announcer in 1936?

3. KDKA has been the Pirates flagship radio station continuously since 1955. What other still-existing station also served that role?

What was (is) the "home run call" for each of the following?

4. Rosey Rowswell

5. Bob Prince

6. Lanny Frattare

7. Who replaced Bob Prince and Nellie King after they were fired following the 1975 season?

8. Which Pirates broadcaster previously did a three year stint as a radio color analyst for the NFL Buffalo Bills?

9. What was the genesis of Pirates broadcaster Jim Rooker's "Unintentional Walk" which raised $81,000 for local charities following the 1989 season?

10. Name the five former Pirates players who later became Pirates broadcasters. (Hint: Four were pitchers.)

Answers

1. Harold Arlin
2. Rosey Rowswell
3. WWSW
4. "Open the window, Aunt Minnie!"
5. "Kiss it goodbye!"
6. "Go ball! Get out of here!"
7. Milo Hamilton and Lanny Frattare
8. Greg Brown
9. The Pirates scored ten runs in the first inning against the Phillies in Philadelphia. Rooker said on the air that he'd walk back to Pittsburgh if the Bucs lost. They did and he did, though not until the off season.
10. Pitchers Nellie King, Jim Rooker, Steve Blass, Bob Walk and third baseman, Don Hoak

FULL SEASON

Sec. 17
Row K
Seat 22
Gate F

"You can never overpay a good player. You can overpay a bad one. I don't mind paying a good player $200,000. What I mind is paying a $20,000 ballplayer $22,000."

–Steelers owner Art Rooney

Gunner Nicknames

Match the following Pirates with their nicknames which were either coined or popularized by Buccos broadcaster, Bob Prince.

1.	Don Hoak	a)	Quail
2.	Dick Schofield	b)	Ducky
3.	Bob Skinner	c)	Road Runner
4.	Vernon Law	d)	Kitten
5.	Harvey Haddix	e)	Clink
6.	Al Oliver	f)	Beetles
7.	Manny Sanguillen	g)	Dog
8.	Bob Bailey	h)	Deacon
9.	Bill Virdon	i)	Tiger
10.	Donn Clendenon	j)	Scoop

Sec. 07

Row 19

Seat 12

Enter
Gate C
Upper Tier

"My only request is that I draw my last dollar and my last breath at precisely the same instant."

–Steelers Hall of Fame quarterback Bobby Layne

FULL SEASON TICKET

Answers

1. I
2. B
3. G
4. H
5. D
6. J
7. C
8. F
9. A
10. E

Sec. 82
Row E
Seat 17

Enter Gate B

"That's pretty good, considering that
Dave's previous idol was himself."

*-Willie Stargell, when told that Pirate
teammate Dave Parker called Stargell
his idol*

The First
All-Black Lineup

Without fanfare, on September 1, 1971 at Three Rivers Stadium, the Pirates turned in a starting lineup card which was later determined to be the first all-black (or all-minority) starting lineup in Major League Baseball history. The attendance was 11,278. The Pirates beat the Phillies, 10-7, and later went on to win the World Series. How many of these nine Buccos can you name? The positions and batting order are provided.

1. Second base
2. Center field
3. Right field
4. Left field
5. Catcher
6. Third base
7. First base
8. Shortstop
9. Pitcher
10. "When is comes to making out the lineup, I'm colorblind." And the manager who said that was _____?

Answers

1. Rennie Stennett (2B)

2. Gene Clines (CF)

3. Roberto Clemente (RF)

4. Willie Stargell (LF)

5. Manny Sanguillen (C)

6. Dave Cash (3B)

7. Al Oliver (1B)

8. Jackie Hernandez (SS)

9. Dock Ellis (P)

10. Danny Murtaugh, the Pirates skipper of that game

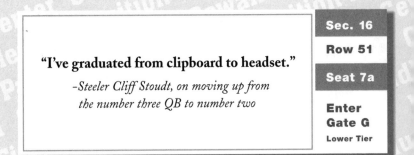

"I've graduated from clipboard to headset."

*-Steeler Cliff Stoudt, on moving up from
the number three QB to number two*

Sec. 16

Row 51

Seat 7a

**Enter
Gate G**
Lower Tier

The Year Was ...

Give the year for each of the following.

1. Franco's Immaculate Reception
2. Clemente's MVP season
3. The last game at Forbes Field
4. The first game at Three Rivers Stadium
5. The Cordova/Rincon no-hitter
6. Willie Stargell's last season
7. Danny Murtaugh's last season
8. Jim Leyland's first season
9. The Penguins consecutive Stanley Cups
10. The Buccos playoff loss to Atlanta on Francisco Cabrera's pinch hit

FULL SEASON
Sec. 17
Row K
Seat 22
Gate F

"I'm going to graduate on time, no matter how long it takes."

–Pitt senior basketball player Rod Brookin

Answers

1. 1972
2. 1966
3. 1970
4. 1970
5. 1997
6. 1982
7. 1976
8. 1986
9. 1991-'92
10. 1992

Sec. 07

Row 19

Seat 12

Enter
Gate C

Upper Tier

FULL SEASON TICKET

"He is complex, confusing, misunderstood, unclear in every way but one: He is a brilliant coach."

-Ken Dryden, on Penguins coach Scotty Bowman

Multi-Sport

1. Which Steelers quarterback played baseball for Jim Leyland in the Florida Instructional League?

2. What former Penguin coached the Pittsburgh Phantoms (roller hockey) in their only year of existence?

3. Name the twins who played sparingly for the Pirates in the fifties, but were better known as college basketball players.

4. Which Major League Baseball team drafted Dan Marino?

5. Who was the Ohio State Heisman Trophy runner-up who spent two mediocre seasons as a Pirate in the fifties?

6. With what NFL teams did Pitt basketball star Sam Clancy play?

7. What position did he play?

8. Who was an All-American basketball star at Duke who played briefly in the NBA, starred at shortstop for the Pirates and later became a radio announcer for Pitt basketball?

9. Name the All-American halfback who pitched for the Pirates in 1959-'60.

10. What three varsity sports did Mike Ditka play at Pitt?

Answers

1. Bubby Brister
2. Rick Kehoe
3. Eddie and Johnnie O'Brien
4. The Kansas City Royals
5. Vic Janowicz
6. The Browns and the Colts
7. Defensive end
8. Dick Groat
9. Paul Geil
10. Football, baseball and basketball

Sec. 82   Row E   Seat 17

Enter Gate B

"Last year we had so many people coming in and out they didn't bother to sew their names on the backs of their uniforms. They just put them there with Velcro."

–Andy Van Slyke, on the 1987 Pirates

TD

1. Where did Tony Dorsett go to high school?

2. Against what team did Dorsett play both his very first and very last games as a Panther?

3. Dorsett became the NCAA all-time leading rusher with a 32-yard TD run against which team?

4. Whose record did he break with that run?

5. That record stood for 22 years. Who finally broke it in 1998?

6. Dorsett was the second overall pick in the 1977 draft. Who was first?

7. What former Steeler did Dorsett displace in the Dallas Cowboys backfield?

8. What NFL record did Dorsett set in 1983 that could be tied, but will never be broken?

9. Which Pitt teammate of Dorsett also had a 1000 yard rushing season?

10. True or false? Dorsett's number 33 was the first Pitt football number to be retired.

Answers

1. Hopewell
2. Georgia Bulldogs
3. Navy
4. Archie Griffin's record
5. Ricky Williams
6. Rick Bell
7. Preston Pearson
8. Longest run from scrimmage (99 yards)
9. Elliot Walker
10. True

Pro Basketball?
In Pittsburgh?

1. What league did the Pittsburgh Rens play for during its only year of existence?

2. The Pittsburgh Pipers were the very first American Basketball Association champs. Whom did they beat?

3. Which Pittsburgh Piper was ABA MVP that championship season?

4. Who was head coach of the champion Pipers?

5. What was unique about the ball used by the Pipers (and the rest of the ABA)?

6. The Pipers moved briefly before returning to Pittsburgh and becoming the Condors. Where?

7. The Pipers had originally planned to change their name to the Pioneers but backed off after a protest from which local school with that same nickname?

8. Which Condor (and former Duquesne Duke) went on to play five seasons for the NBA Milwaukee Bucks?

9. The Pittsburgh Piranhas of the Continental Basketball League went all the way to the finals in their single year of existence. To whom did they lose?

10. Which longtime area broadcaster was the radio "voice of the Piranhas"?

Answers

1. The American Basketball League
2. The New Orleans Buccaneers
3. Connie Hawkins
4. Vince Cazzetta
5. It was red, white and blue.
6. Minneapolis (as the Minnesota Pipers)
7. Point Park
8. Mickey Davis
9. The always tough Yakima Sun Kings
10. Ray Goss

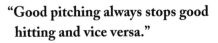

"Good pitching always stops good hitting and vice versa."

-Pirates southpaw Bob Veale

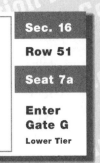

Sec. 16

Row 51

Seat 7a

**Enter
Gate G**

Lower Tier

The Buccos of October

1. Who pitched for the 1960 Pirates and was pitching coach for the 1979 team?

2. In which two World Series did the Bucs overcome a three-games-to-one deficit?

3. Who was on deck when Maz hit the big one in 1960?

4. Which Pirates World Series featured the National League batting champ and his American League counterpart?

5. What former Pirates star went 1-for-3 as a pinch hitter for the Yanks in the 1960 Series?

6. The Pirates played in the very first World Series. What was the year?

7. Who drove in the winning run of the 1971 Series?

8. Who scored that run?

9. In what World Series did the Pirates fall in four?

10. How many World Series did Honus Wagner play in?

Answers

1. Harvey Haddix
2. 1925 (against the Senators) and 1979 (against the Orioles)
3. Dick Stuart
4. Honus Wagner and Ty Cobb in 1909
5. Dale Long
6. 1903
7. Jose Pagan
8. Willie Stargell
9. They lost to the legendary 1927 New York Yankees.
10. Two, losing to Boston in 1903 and beating Detroit in 1909

FULL SEASON

Sec. 17 Row K Seat 22 Gate F

"People ask me why we didn't sign David Cone. Heck, we can't even afford an ice-cream cone."

-Pirates manager Jim Leyland

Simply Super

1. When the Steelers won their fourth Super Bowl they broke the record of three held by which team?

2. For Super Bowl XXX, Kordell Stewart was listed third on the depth chart for what position?

3. Which Steeler was hospitalized with pleurisy prior to Super Bowl IX, losing 18 pounds, yet still started?

4. Which two Steelers scored safeties in a Super Bowl?

5. How did the Vikings score their only six points in Super Bowl IX?

6. Who is the only Steeler to be named Super Bowl MVP twice?

7. Who were the other two Super Bowl MVPs?

8. Who is the only assistant coach to participate in all five Steelers Super Bowls?

9. Jack Ham has four rings but saw action in only three of the games. Which Bowl did he sit out due to injury?

10. What was the halftime score of Super Bowl IX?

Answers

1. The Steelers
2. Wide receiver
3. Dwight White
4. Dwight White in IX and Reggie Harrison in X
5. A blocked putt was recovered in the end zone.
6. Terry Bradshaw in XIII and XIV
7. Franco Harris in IX and Lynn Swann in X
8. Dick Hoak
9. Super Bowl XIV
10. Steelers – 2, Vikings - 0

Sec. 07

Row 19

Seat 12

Enter
Gate C

Upper Tier

FULL SEASON TICKET

"He used to have a bed check just
for me every night. No problem.
The bed was always there."

*–Pirates hurler Jim Rooker, on manager
Chuck Tanner*

The Other Guys

1. In 1963 Pete Rose got the very first of his 4256 career hits off which Pirates righty?

2. Who hit his 500th career homer off Don Robinson at Three Rivers Stadium?

3. Which opposing player hit two of the homers that cleared the right field roof at Forbes Field?

4. Which opposing player has two of the 13 upper deck homers at Three Rivers Stadium?

5. Which Philadelphia Phillie turned an unassisted triple play against the Pirates at Three Rivers Stadium in 1992?

6. Who pitched the first no-hitter at Three Rivers Stadium?

7. Which American Leaguer hit an upper decker during the Home Run Hitting Contest before the 1994 All-Star Game?

8. How many of Mark McGwire's record 70 homers were hit at Three Rivers Stadium in 1998?

9. How many of Sammy Sosa's 66 were hit there that same season?

10. Who was the MVP of the 1960 World Series?

Answers

1. Bob Friend

2. Mike Schmidt

3. Eddie Mathews of the Braves

4. Jeff Bagwell of the Astros

5. Mickey Morandini

6. Bob Gibson of the Cardinals

7. Frank Thomas

8. Two – Numbers 52 and 53 off Francisco Cordova and Ricardo Rincon, respectively

9. Two – Numbers 57 and 58 off Jason Schmidt and Sean Lawrence, respectively

10. Bobby Richardson of the Yankees

Sec.	Row	Seat
82	E	17

Enter Gate B

"No – the next Barry Bonds."

–Steelers running back Barry Foster, when asked if he'd like his infant son to be the next Barry Foster

Pittsburgh Pugilism

1. At what facility did Billy Conn beat Mario Bettina to win the light-heavyweight championship?

2. Who beat Gene Tunney for the light-heavyweight championship in 1922?

3. Did Billy Conn and Fritzie Zivic ever face each other in a pro bout?

4. Larry Holmes survived a seventh-round knockdown while successfully defending his heavyweight title against whom at the Civic Arena in 1981?

5. Who was the ring announcer for that fight?

6. Prior to the Holmes fight, who fought in the last heavyweight championship bout held in Pittsburgh?

7. Jake LaMotta, Henry Armstrong and Beau Jack were among the losers to this Lawrenceville champ.

8. Whom did Monessen's Michael Moorer defeat to become heavyweight champ?

9. Whom did he lose the title to?

10. After losing his first fight with Joe Louis, Billy Conn said he knew "Uncle Mike" would give him another chance. To whom was he referring?

Answers

1. Madison Square Garden

2. Harry Greb

3. Yes, Conn won a 10-round decision in 1936.

4. Renaldo Snipes

5. Myron Cope

6. Jersey Joe Walcott knocked out Ezzard Charles to win the title in 1951.

7. Fritzie Zivic

8. Evander Holyfield

9. George Foreman

10. Promoter Mike Jacobs

"I always thought of Pittsburgh as a dirty city and a blue-collar town. And that's exactly what I think of their football team."

–Jean Fugett

Sec. 16

Row 51

Seat 7a

Enter
Gate G

Lower Tier

Put Me In Coach

1. Which two Steelers head coaches also served in that capacity at Pitt?

2. In 1995 Bill Cowher became the youngest head coach to lead his team to a Super Bowl. How old was he?

3. True or false? At the time of his hiring Chuck Noll was the NFL's youngest head coach.

4. True or false? At the time of his hiring Bill Cowher was the NFL's youngest head coach.

5. For which two teams was Noll an assistant coach before coming to the Steelers?

6. For which two teams was Cowher an assistant coach?

7. Where did the Steelers play during Noll's first season?

8. Name the only two Steelers coaches (other than Noll and Cowher) whose career win-loss percentage is over .500.

9. True or false? When he retired, Chuck Noll had more wins than all previous Steelers coaches combined.

10. Who is third in career wins among Steelers coaches behind Noll and Cowher?

Answers

1. Jock Sutherland and Johnny Michelosen

2. 38

3. True

4. True

5. San Diego Chargers and Baltimore Colts

6. Cleveland Browns and Kansas City Royals

7. Pitt Stadium

8. Buddy Parker (.514) and Jock Sutherland (.563)

9. True – Noll was 209-163-1. The others (over 35 years) were a combined 161-256-20.

10. Buddy Parker, 51-48-6

FULL SEASON

Sec. 17
Row K
Seat 22
Gate F

"Maybe now he'll get a complete game."

–Pirates coach Rich Donnelly, on retired pitcher Bob Walk's assignment to the broadcast booth

The Great One

1. How many career regular season hits did Roberto Clemente have?

2. What opposing player, who already had over 3000 hits, congratulated Clemente after he hit his 3000th?

3. Who pinch ran for Clemente after his 3000th hit?

4. Clemente was first signed by what major league organization?

5. Who was the executive for that team who first spotted him?

6. On July 25, 1956 Clemente hit a grand slam in the ninth at Forbes Field to beat the Cubs, 9-8. What was unusual about that homer?

7. In how many World Series games did Clemente hit safely?

8. Clemente's batting average in his 1966 MVP season was the same number as his final career average. What was it?

9. Who started in right field on Opening Day, 1973, the first home game after the death of Roberto Clemente?

10. What message was shown on the digital clock on Mount Washington across the river from Three Rivers Stadium after Clemente died?

Answers

1. 3000
2. Willie Mays
3. Bill Mazeroski
4. The Dodgers
5. Al Campanis
6. It was an inside-the-park homer.
7. All seven in both the 1960 and 1971 Series for a total of 14
8. .317
9. Manny Sanguillen
10. "Adios Amigo"

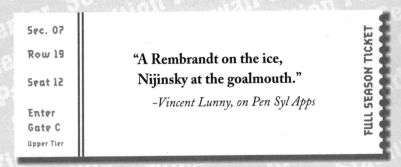

Sec. 07

Row 19

Seat 12

Enter
Gate C
Upper Tier

FULL SEASON TICKET

"A Rembrandt on the ice,
Nijinsky at the goalmouth."

-Vincent Lunny, on Pen Syl Apps

Magnifique!!!

1. Mario Lemieux was NHL Rookie of the Year for 1984-'85, winning what trophy?

2. How many seasons did it take the Pens to make the playoffs after Mario joined the team?

3. How many times was Mario the All-Star Game MVP?

4. How many times was he named Dapper Dan Man of the Year?

5. How many Hart Trophies (NHL MVP) does he have?

6. How many times did he win the Art Ross Trophy as the league's leading scorer?

7. How many career regular season goals does Mario have?

8. Which season did Mario sit out for health reasons?

9. On New Year's Eve, 1988 Mario scored five goals against the Devils. How did this make NHL history?

10. The waiting period for the Hall of Fame was waived in 1997 for Mario, only the ninth time in history this was done. Who was the last player this was done for?

Answers

1. The Calder Memorial Trophy

2. Five

3. Three (1985, 1988 and 1990)

4. Twice (1986 and 1989)

5. Three (1987-'88, 1992-'93 and 1995-'96)

6. Five (1987-'88, 1988-'89, 1991-'92, 1992-'93 and 1995-'96)

7. 613

8. 1994-'95

9. He was the first player in NHL history to score a goal five ways in one game (even strength, power play, short handed, penalty shot and empty net).

10. Bobby Orr in 1979

Uniformity

1. In 1952 the Pirates first began wearing what now standard piece of equipment?

2. The Pirates added last names to the back of the jerseys in 1977. They remained with the single exception of which season?

3. Which NHL team protested the Penguins' switch to black and gold in the City of Champions year of 1980?

4. What were the Pens original colors?

5. The Pirates went to black and gold in 1948, replacing what colors?

6. The Pirates, and other teams, went to flattop caps in 1976. The other teams dropped them the following year, but the Pirates kept them until when?

7. What were the colors of the ABA champion Pittsburgh Pipers?

8. What colors did they switch to when they became the Condors?

9. From the player's perspective, which side of the helmet is the Steelers logo on?

10. In 1979 the NHL made helmets mandatory for new players. Which one-time Penguin was one of the last five "men without hats" exempt from this rule still playing into the nineties?

Answers

1. Batting helmets
2. 1995
3. The Boston Bruins
4. Dark blue, light blue and white
5. Blue and red
6. 1987
7. Orange and blue
8. Red and gold
9. The right side
10. Randy Carlyle

Sec. | Row | Seat
82 | E | 17
Enter Gate B

"It's like watching Mario Andretti park a car."

-Pirates Hall of Famer Ralph Kiner, as a New York Mets announcer, describing Phil Niekro's knuckleball

The Nicknames

Name the Pittsburgh sports figures
known by each of the following monikers.

1. The Old Ranger
2. The Flying Dutchman
3. The Possum
4. The Emperor
5. The Kitten
6. The Gunner
7. The Whistling Irishman
8. The Pittsburgh Kid
9. The Pittsburgh Windmill
10. The Deacon

**"They had better defense at
Pearl Harbor."**

*-Andy Van Slyke, talking about
the Pirates*

Sec. 16

Row 51

Seat 7a

**Enter
Gate G**
Lower Tier

Answers

1. Ray Mansfield
2. Honus Wagner
3. Jim Woods
4. Chuck Noll
5. Harvey Haddix
6. Bob Prince
7. Danny Murtaugh
8. Billy Conn
9. Harry Greb
10. Vernon Law

FULL SEASON

Sec. 17
Row K
Seat 22
Gate F

"You can have money stacked to the ceiling, but the size of your funeral is still going to depend on the weather."

–Pirates manager Chuck Tanner

Bucs in the Hall

1. The five original inductees to the Baseball Hall of Fame in 1936 included which Pittsburgh Pirate?

2. Who were the next two Pirates to make it to the Hall, both in 1945?

3. Which Buccos Hall of Famer holds the record for most hits by a rookie?

4. Who finally broke Buccos Hall of Famer Arky Vaughan's National League batting average record set in 1935?

5. Name the five Pirates Hall of Famers who have had their uniform numbers retired by the team.

6. Who is the only Pirates player to have his number retired who is not in the Hall of Fame (though he should be)?

7. Which Pirates Hall of Famer was a player-manager for the team for 15 seasons, compiling the best career winning percentage of any Buc skipper (.595), while batting .315 lifetime?

8. The five year waiting period was waived when Roberto Clemente entered the Hall in 1973, only the second time this was done. Who was it previously done for?

9. Which Pirates Hall of Famer (who also played for the Dodgers) led the league in stolen bases for ten seasons?

10. How old was Willie Stargell during his MVP season of 1979?

Answers

1. Honus Wagner
2. Fred Clarke and Pie Traynor
3. Lloyd Waner (223 in 1927)
4. Tony Gwynn in 1994
5. Honus Wagner, Pie Traynor, Ralph Kiner, Roberto Clemente and Willie Stargell
6. Bill Mazeroski
7. Fred Clarke
8. Lou Gehrig in 1939
9. Max Carey
10. 39

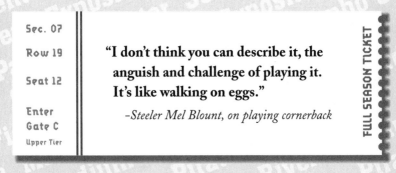

Sec. 07

Row 19

Seat 12

Enter
Gate C
Upper Tier

"I don't think you can describe it, the anguish and challenge of playing it. It's like walking on eggs."

–Steeler Mel Blount, on playing cornerback

FULL SEASON TICKET

Arnie

1. In what year did Arnold Palmer win the U.S. Amateur title?

2. What was Arnie's first pro tournament win?

3. What up-and-comer beat Arnie in 18-hole playoff at the U.S. Open at Oakmont?

4. True or false? Arnie won the U.S. Senior Open on his very first try.

5. In which four years did Arnie win the Masters?

6. Arnie won the U.S. Open in Denver in 1960 with a 65 in the final round. How many strokes behind was he after the first three rounds?

7. What is Arnie's home course?

8. What is the only major tournament that Arnie never won?

9. True or false? Arnie is the first golfer to reach the million dollar mark in winnings.

10. Did Arnie's wife ever appear on *The Tonight Show*?

Sec. Row Seat
82 E 17
Enter Gate B

"I couldn't understand a word Coach (Johnny) Majors said, but I sure liked the way he said it."

-Tony Dorsett, on being recruited by the University of Pittsburgh

Answers

1. 1954

2. The Canadian Open in 1955 – He won $2000.

3. Jack Nicklaus

4. True

5. 1958, 1960, 1962 and 1964

6. Seven

7. Latrobe Country Club

8. The PGA

9. True

10. NO! That's just a silly rumor.

Sec.	Row	Seat
82	E	17

Enter Gate B

"Trying to hit him was like trying to drink coffee with a fork."

–Willie Stargell, on facing Sandy Koufax

Buccos of the Century

The 100th Anniversary All-Time Pirates Team was chosen in a poll by the *Pittsburgh Press* in 1987. How many can you name? The positions are given.

      1. MGR

      2. LHP

      3. RHP

      4. REL

      5. C

      6. 1B

      7. 2B

      8. SS

      9. 3B

      10. Three outfielders

"Shorter runways. Buses have a hard time taking off on short runways."

–Pierre Larouche, on what he thought was the best part of being back in the NHL after playing in the minors

Sec. 16

Row 51

Seat 7a

Enter Gate G

Lower Tier

Answers

1. Danny Murtaugh
2. Harvey Haddix
3. Vernon Law
4. ElRoy Face
5. Manny Sanguillen
6. Willie Stargell
7. Bill Mazeroski
8. Honus Wagner
9. Pie Traynor
10. Roberto Clemente, Paul Waner and Ralph Kiner

Remember Those Fabulous Maulers

1. The Pittsburgh Maulers home opener against the Birmingham Stallions was the only sellout in United States Football League history. Why?

2. Which Pitt player was the very first draft choice of the USFL?

3. Four former Steelers played for the Michigan Panthers. How many can you name?

4. Which New York Jets cornerback jumped to the Maulers?

5. The Maulers were 3-15 during their only season. Two of those victories came against which team?

6. The Maulers went through three head coaches in one year. One began the season, one finished it and a third was hired for the next season, which never came. Who were they?

7. What Pitt All-American basketball player was a defensive end for the Maulers?

8. Mauler Mike Rozier was one of three consecutive Heisman Trophy winners to choose the USFL. Who were the other two?

9. What NFL team did Rozier go to after the Maulers disbanded?

10. Maulers starting quarterback Glenn Carano was previously a backup for which NFL team?

Answers

1. The Stallions quarterback was Pittsburgh boo-bird favorite, Cliff Stoudt.

2. Dan Marino – He chose the Miami Dolphins over the L.A. Express.

3. Ray Pinney, Thom Dornbrook, John Banaszak and Tyrone McGriff

4. Jerry Holmes

5. The Washington Federals

6. Joe Pendry, Ellis Rainsberger and Hank Bullough, respectively

7. Sam Clancy

8. Herschel Walker and Doug Flutie

9. The Houston Oilers

10. The Dallas Cowboys

FULL SEASON

Sec. 17
Row K
Seat 22
Gate F

"He's the only man I know who will hit you in the mouth and bless you at the same time."

–Steelers offensive tackle Leon Searcy, about Green Bay All-Pro linebacker and ordained minister Reggie White

The Steel Hall

1. In what year was Steelers founder Art Rooney inducted into the Football Hall of Fame?

2. Which Steeler went to the Hall in 1969, his first year of eligibility?

3. In 1987 Joe Greene was inducted into the Hall with which other Steeler? (Hint: He was presented by Art Rooney.)

4. Which quarterback, who spent part of his career with the Steelers, was also inducted in 1987?

5. Many fans were upset that Terry Bradshaw did not choose someone from the Steelers organization to present him at his Hall of Fame induction. Whom did he choose?

6. The first NFL commissioner was a charter inductee to the Hall. He was also once a co-owner of the Steelers. Who is he?

7. Two Steelers Hall of Famers both played for and coached the team. Who are they?

8. Name the only Steelers coach in the Hall who was not also a Steelers player.

9. Who was the first of the Super Steelers of the seventies to make it to the Hall?

10. Who was the last?

Answers

1. In 1964, the Hall's second year of existence

2. Ernie Stautner

3. John Henry Johnson

4. Len Dawson (a Steeler from 1957-'59)

5. Vern Lundquist, his broadcast partner

6. Bert Bell

7. Johnny "Blood" McNally (player – 1934, 1937-'39; coach – 1937-'39) and Walt Keisling (player – 1937-'39; coach – 1939-'40, 1941-'44, 1954-'56)

8. Chuck Noll

9. Joe Greene in 1987

10. Mike Webster in 1997

Sec. 07

Row 19

Seat 12

Enter
Gate C

Upper Tier

FULL SEASON TICKET

"We don't want jazz musicians.
We want classical musicians."

–Steelers coach Chuck Noll, on scrambling
quarterbacks

Gunnerisms

Translate the following into the colorful phrases
made so familiar to Pirates fans by Bob Prince.

1. A very high pop fly
2. A base hit followed by a home run
3. An extra base hit on artificial turf
4. Very close
5. Even closer
6. A double play that empties the bases
7. A pitch so fast it could seemingly be heard but not seen
8. It's a home run (hit by a Bucco, of course).
9. A routine fly ball
10. The game is over and the Pirates win.

Sec.	Row	Seat	
82	E	17	Enter Gate B

"On Father's Day, we again wish you all
happy birthday."

*–Pirates Hall of Famer and New York Mets
broadcaster, Ralph Kiner*

Answers

1. Home run in an elevator shaft
2. A bloop and a blast
3. A bug on the rug
4. A gnat's eyelash
5. The fuzz on a tick's ear
6. A Hoover (as in vacuum)
7. A radio ball
8. Kiss it goodbye!
9. A can of corn
10. We had 'em all the way!

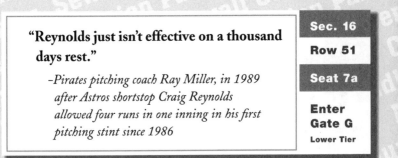

"Reynolds just isn't effective on a thousand days rest."

–*Pirates pitching coach Ray Miller, in 1989 after Astros shortstop Craig Reynolds allowed four runs in one inning in his first pitching stint since 1986*

Sec. 16

Row 51

Seat 7a

Enter
Gate G
Lower Tier

Who 'Dat? II

1. In 1980, subbing for the injured Dan Marino, he led the Panthers to a 30-6 victory against the Johnny Majors-coached Tennessee Vols.

2. He is a Hall of Fame baseball broadcaster and TV personality who was a catcher for the Pirates in the early fifties.

3. This former Bucco grew up as a family friend of the Clementes and was named for fellow Puerto Rican Orlando Cepeda.

4. When he was traded to the Giants in 1987 he became the last member of the 1979 "We Are Family" champs to leave the team.

5. In 1979 he was moved from the mound to left field for a single batter, but ended up catching a fly out to end the game.

6. He went 7 for 7 against the Cubs in 1975.

7. His single season with the Pirates (1969) was not as memorable as his marriage to sex goddess Mamie Van Doren.

8. In parts of four seasons with the Pirates (1978-'81) he had only 27 at bats but scored 36 runs.

9. When he left the Steelers in 1990 he was the last player with a Super Bowl ring from a Steelers victory.

10. In 1981 he gave up a single to the leadoff batter, then retired the next 27 batters while pitching for the Pirates.

Answers

1. Rick Trocano
2. Joe Garagiola
3. Orlando Merced
4. Don Robinson
5. Kent Tekulve
6. Rennie Stennett
7. Bo Belinski
8. Matt Alexander (a pinch running specialist)
9. Dwayne Woodruff
10. Jim Bibby

FULL SEASON

Sec. 17
Row K
Seat 22
Gate F

"Anaheim left winger Paul Kariya, whose father is Japanese, is believed to be the only NHL player whose middle name is 'Tetsuhiko'."

-Pittsburgh Post-Gazette *writer Dave Molinari*

Gazing at
the All-Stars II

1. Who was the only player to participate in both All-Star Games at Forbes Field? (Hint: He wasn't a Bucco.)

2. Who played for the American League in 1959 and managed the National League in 1974?

3. Who threw out the first ball at the 1959 All-Star Game?

4. Who was the third base coach who waved in the winning run of the 1994 All-Star Game?

5. In 1960 the Buccos were represented by a team record eight All-Stars. How many can you name?

6. Which Pirate is the only player ever to steal home in an All-Star Game?

7. Which Pirates shortstop was the first player to hit two home runs in the same All-Star Game?

8. Two Pirates made a team-record eight <u>consecutive</u> All-Star appearances. Who were they?

9. Which Pirates outfielder made it to a team record 12 All-Star Games?

10. At which Pittsburgh All-Star Game was the legendary comedy trio, The Three Stooges, among the spectators?

Answers

1. Stan Musial

2. Yogi Berra (played for the Yankees in 1959, managed the Mets in 1974)

3. Vice-president Richard Nixon

4. Pirates manager Jim Leyland

5. Smoky Burgess, Roberto Clemente, ElRoy Face, Bob Friend, Dick Groat, Vernon Law, Bill Mazeroski and Bob Skinner

6. Pie Traynor (1934)

7. Arkey Vaughan (1941)

8. Arky Vaughan (1934-'41) and Roberto Clemente (1960-'67)

9. Roberto Clemente (1960-'67, 1969-'72)

10. 1959 – They were appearing at the Holiday House at the time.

Steelers Stumpers II

1. Which Steeler was the first NFL player to qualify for a pension without playing in a single game?

2. Who holds the Steelers single game passing yardage record with 409 yards?

3. Who is second with 377?

4. Who filled in for the injured Roy Gerela as the Steelers kicker at the end of the 1976 season?

5. The Steelers were one of the teams that formed the scouting combine BLESTO. What do those initials stand for?

6. Which Steelers star receiver was traded for a player who never wore a Steelers uniform?

7. Terry Bradshaw's last game was also a "last" for the New York Jets. What was it?

8. Who caught Bradshaw's last pass?

9. The Steelers all-time leading scorer, Gary Anderson, was picked up in 1982 after being cut by which team?

10. Name the Steelers linebacker who played for 12 seasons, beginning two years after Super Bowl XIV and ending two years before Super Bowl XXX.

Answers

1. Cliff Stoudt
2. Bobby Layne, against the Chicago Cardinals in 1958
3. Neil O'Donnell, against the Bengals in 1995
4. Ray Mansfield
5. Bears Lions Eagles Steelers Talent Organization
6. Buddy Dial (for Scott Appleton, who chose the AFL)
7. It was their last game at Shea Stadium.
8. Calvin Sweeney
9. The Buffalo Bills
10. Bryan Hinkle

Sec. 07

Row 19

Seat 12

Enter
Gate C
Upper Tier

FULL SEASON TICKET

"Pittsburgh Steelers fans lead the league in collective lunacy. Their elevators don't stop at the top floor."

–Sportscaster Tim McCarver

Buccos Brainteasers II

1. Who replaced Dave Parker in right field when he left the team?

2. Kent Tekulve pitched in 772 games as a Pirate, second only to Roy Face. Did he ever start a game for the Bucs?

3. What future Pirates slugger hit 66 homers in the minors for the Lincoln, Nebraska franchise of the Western League?

4. What was the name of Maury Wills' short-lived downtown nightspot?

5. What former Pirate became the owner of a longtime Oakland tavern bearing his name?

6. Who is the Pirates pitcher who later claimed he was on LSD while pitching a no-hitter in San Diego?

7. That no-hitter was far from perfect. How many Padres reached base?

8. Who was the longtime American League slugger who spent the final season of his career as a Pirate, hitting 25 homers, second on the team only to Ralph Kiner's 51?

9. How did Harvey Haddix make baseball history on May 26, 1959?

10. Who was the last Pirates knuckleballer?

Answers

1. Doug Frobel
2. No
3. Dick Stuart (in 1956)
4. The Stolen Base
5. Frank Gustine
6. Dock Ellis
7. Nine, on eight walks and a hit batter
8. Hank Greenburg
9. He pitched 12 perfect innings against the Braves only to lose in the 13th.
10. Tim Wakefield

Sec.	Row	Seat
82	E	17

Enter Gate B

"Aren't all coaches interim coaches?"

–Penguins executive Wren Blair

By Any Other Name II

Again, the answers to the following are not generally known by their given first names, which are provided in the clues.

1. Oail (yes, Oail) was an NFL head coach who once had his hat grabbed from his head following a loss at Three Rivers Stadium. He subsequently received more than fifty letters from Steelers fans apologizing for the incident.

2. One-time Pirate Richard is the only major leaguer who participated in all four baseball strikes.

3. Robert homered off Met Dwight Gooden as new manager Jim Leyland's very first batter on Opening Day, 1986.

4. Aldege was a goalie for the Pittsburgh Hornets and later became general manager of the Penguins.

5. Until his death Maurice, a Duquesne alumnus, was well known in political as well as sports circles for the tireless support of his alma mater's basketball team.

6. Byron was the first rookie since Franco to lead the team for the season in total yards from scrimmage.

7. Eugene was a tackle for the NFL champ Colts before moving to the Steelers for the 1961-'62 seasons.

8. John once rushed for a team record 218 yards against Philadelphia.

9. Bill's band provided the entertainment at the Steelers fiftieth anniversary banquet.

10. John was the first Pirate to hit 100 career homers.

Answers

1. Bum Phillips
2. Goose Gossage
3. RJ Reynolds
4. Baz Bastein
5. Mossie Murphy
6. Bam Morris
7. Big Daddy Lipscomb
8. Frenchy Fuqua
9. Count Basie
10. Honus Wagner

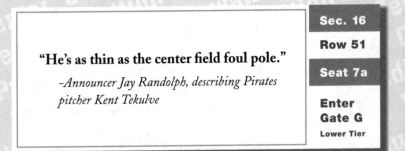

"He's as thin as the center field foul pole."

-Announcer Jay Randolph, describing Pirates pitcher Kent Tekulve

Sec. 16

Row 51

Seat 7a

Enter
Gate G

Lower Tier

Friendly Facilities II

1. What was the Pirates' home park before Forbes Field?

2. What year were the right field stands erected at Forbes Field?

3. What was the pro team that often drew larger crowds than the Penguins at the Civic Arena in 1984?

4. Who did Duquesne beat, 78-40, in the first college basketball game held at the arena in 1961?

5. Who did Pitt lose to, 66-64, on February 15, 1981 in front of 15,824, then the largest sports crowd in Civic Arena history?

6. What college team played its home games at the Arena from 1964-'89?

7. Where did Pitt play its home football games before Pitt Stadium opened in 1925?

8. What Pirates Hall of Famer threw out the ceremonial first pitch at the opening of Three Rivers Stadium?

9. What watch company had its name on the Forbes Field clock?

10. At what Pittsburgh venue did the heavyweight boxing title change hands in 1951?

Answers

1. Exposition Park
2. 1925
3. The indoor soccer Pittsburgh Spirit
4. Carnegie Tech
5. Duquesne
6. Duquesne
7. Forbes Field
8. Pie Traynor
9. Longines
10. Forbes Field

FULL SEASON

Sec. 17
Row K
Seat 22
Gate F

"Ballplayers and deer hunters are alike. They both want the big bucks."

–Pirates GM Larry Doughty, after hunting with three of his players: Sid Bream, John Smiley and Bob Walk

Quotables

Below are ten quotes along with who said them.
See if you know who each was talking about.

1. "He's not a flashy manager, but he always has a reason – a sound reason – for everything he does."   *-Joe L. Brown*

2. "He knows so much about this game it gets scary."
                                        -Rollie Dotsch

3. "He's the finest man I've ever known."
                    -Supreme Court Justice Byron White

4. "[He] dominates a game more than anyone I have seen since Dick Butkus dominated games for Illinois and the Chicago Bears in the sixties."   *-Army coach Ed Cavanaugh*

5. "One time I was on [his] radio show. I didn't understand a word. I just answered the questions, 'Yes,' 'No,' 'I think so.' "
                                        -Mario Lemieux

6. "He'd have lived a hell of a lot longer if he didn't have to play Pittsburgh six times in two years."
                    -Bum Phillips (pre-writing an epitaph)

7. "I'm in and [he] isn't. It's unbelievable."
        -Charley Feeney (longtime Post-Gazette *baseball writer upon making the writers' wing of the Hall of Fame)*

8. "When I saw our scouting reports of the Pirates I couldn't believe what was said of [him] … I accused my scouts of watching Superman movies instead of the Pirates."   *-Casey Stengel*

9. "We finished last with you. We can finish last without you."
                                        -Branch Rickey

10. "He'd stick thumbs in your eyes, rub gloves over your sores and fight you every which way."   *-Henry Armstrong*

Answers

1. Danny Murtaugh
2. Chuck Noll
3. Art Rooney
4. Hugh Green
5. Myron Cope
6. Himself
7. Bill Mazeroski
8. Roberto Clemente
9. Ralph Kiner
10. Fritzie Zivic

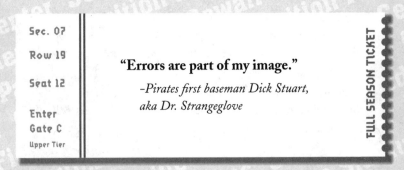

Sec. 07
Row 19
Seat 12
Enter
Gate C
Upper Tier

"Errors are part of my image."

*-Pirates first baseman Dick Stuart,
aka Dr. Strangeglove*

FULL SEASON TICKET

Digital Retirement

The Steelers do not officially retire numbers but seven have long been unavailable through the policy of longtime equipment manager, Tony Parisi. All were previously worn by Super Steelers of the seventies.

1. What was the first number to be retired by the Pirates?

2. The Pirates retired number 33 for Honus Wagner, which he wore as a coach, never as a player. Why?

3. What is the only number to be retired by two different Pittsburgh pro sports teams?

4. Who was the last player to wear number 75 before Joe Greene?

5. Who was the last player to wear number 12 before Terry Bradshaw?

6. Who are the only two Penguins to have their numbers retired?

7. Who was the last Pirates player before Roberto Clemente to wear number 21? (Hint: He spent many subsequent years in baseball, though not as a player.)

8. When the Pirates retired Ralph Kiner's number 4 in 1987, which then current Bucco had to give it up?

9. When the Pirates retired Pie Traynor's number 20 in 1970, which then current Bucco had to give it up?

10. Tony Dorsett's number 33 was the first Pitt football number to be retired. Which later players were numbers 13, 99 and 79 retired for?

Answers

1. Manager Billy Meyer's number 1 (in 1954)

2. They didn't wear numbers in those days.

3. Michel Briere of the Penguins and Roberto Clemente of the Pirates both wore number 21.

4. Tackle Ken Kortas (1965-'66)

5. Quarterback Terry Nofsinger (1963-'64)

6. Michel Briere (21) and Mario Lemieux (66)

7. Former Pirates and Atlanta Braves trainer, Tony Bartirome

8. Mike LaValliere

9. Richie Hebner

10. Dan Marino (13), Hugh Green (99) and Bill Fralic (79)

College Nicknames

Match the following area colleges and universities
with their athletic team nicknames.

1.	Allegheny College	a) Redhawks
2.	California University of Pennsylvania	b) Indians
3.	Indiana University of Pennsylvania	c) Gators
4.	Slippery Rock University	d) Vulcans
5.	Carnegie Mellon University	e) Rockets
6.	Duquesne University	f) Pioneers
7.	Point Park College	g) Panthers
8.	Robert Morris College	h) Colonials
9.	University of Pittsburgh	i) Dukes
10.	LaRoche College	j) Tartans

Sec. 82   Row E   Seat 17   Enter Gate B

"One of the nice things about golf is that
nobody slams into you when you're in
the backswing."

–Pittsburgh Penguin Pierre Larouche

Answers

1. C
2. D
3. B
4. E
5. J
6. I
7. F
8. H
9. G
10. A

"We never knew what we were going to look like. One day, we'd look like bumblebees. The next day you couldn't see us. Then we'd look like a bunch of taxicabs running around the field."

–Third baseman Phil Garner, on the many uniform combinations of the Pirates in the late 1970s

Sec. 16

Row 51

Seat 7a

Enter
Gate G

Lower Tier

First Of All –
Second Time Around

1. Who threw out the first ceremonial first pitch at Three Rivers Stadium?

2. Who was the first amateur athlete to be named Dapper Dan Man of the Year?

3. Who was the first female to sit on the dais at the Dapper Dan Banquet?

4. In what year was the Pirates first night home opener?

5. What Pirate hit the first home run in World Series history?

6. What opposing pitcher gave up that home run?

7. Who was the first black player for the Pirates?

8. Who was the first black player for the Steelers?

9. What future Pirate was the first member of the expansion Kansas City Royals to hit two homers in a game?

10. Chuck Cooper became the first black player to be drafted by the NBA when he was chosen by the Boston Celtics in 1950. Which local college did he play for?

Answers

1. Pie Traynor

2. Tony Dorsett

3. Evonne Goolagong of the Pittsburgh Triangles (World Team Tennis)

4. 1985

5. Jimmy Sebring

6. Cy Young of the Boston Pilgrims

7. Curt Roberts (1954)

8. Former Duquesne Duke Ray Kemp was a tackle on the very first Steeler team in 1933 and later became athletic director at Tennessee State.

9. Pitcher Jim Rooker in 1969 – Both were off Jim Kaat of the Twins.

10. Duquesne

FULL SEASON

Sec. 17
Row K
Seat 22
Gate F

"A committee is usually a group of uninformed, appointed by the unwilling to accomplish the unnecessary."

–Pirates general manager Syd Thrift

Pittsburgh Potpourri II

1. Who was the Steelers very first draft choice ever – Charles Dickens, Ernest Hemingway, William Shakespeare or Stephen King?

2. Which of the following was a backup linebacker for the Steelers in Super Bowls IX and X – Mike Wallace, Ed Bradley, Leslie Stahl or Andy Rooney?

3. In what cities were the Steelers four victorious Super Bowls played?

4. Name the four world champion pro teams to call the Civic Arena home.

5. Pirate Dale Long homered in eight consecutive games in 1956, a record since tied by which two American Leaguers?

6. With whom did Willie Stargell share the 1979 National League MVP award?

7. Which four Steelers once shared the cover of *Time* magazine?

8. Which two men were *Sports Illustrated's* Sportsmen of the Year in 1979?

9. Ralph Kiner won or shared the National League home run title in all of his seven full seasons as a Pirate. Name the two players he shared it with, one sharing it twice.

10. Let's get politically correct: Name a sixties Pirates pitcher who is the only U.S. senator to pitch a perfect game; a member of the 1960 Pirates who was later elected to the U.S. House of Representatives; and a former Steeler who ran for vice-president of the U.S.

Answers

1. Shakespeare – He was a Notre Dame back.

2. Bradley

3. IX in New Orleans, X and XIII in Miami and XIV in Pasadena

4. The Penguins (NHL), Pipers (ABA), Triangles (World Team Tennis) and the Hornets (AHL)

5. Don Mattingly and Ken Griffey Jr.

6. Keith Hernandez

7. The Front Four: Joe Greene, LC Greenwood, Ernie Holmes and Dwight White

8. Willie Stargell and Terry Bradshaw

9. Johnny Mize (1947-'48) and Hank Sauer (1952)

10. Jim Bunning, Wilmer "Vinegar Bend" Mizell and Jack Kemp, respectively

---

Sec. 07

Row 19

Seat 12

Enter
Gate C

Upper Tier

FULL SEASON TICKET

"They ought to pay me just to walk around here."

–Pirate Dave Parker, proclaiming himself the "foundation" of the club

Closing It Out

With what pro team did each of the following
end their playing careers?

1. Ralph Kiner
2. Bob Friend
3. John Candelaria
4. Connie Hawkins
5. Randy Carlyle
6. Mike Webster
7. ElRoy Face
8. Franco Harris
9. John Henry Johnson
10. Kent Tekulve

Sec. 82   Row E   Seat 17   Enter Gate B

**"I eat them all. Hey, the teeth are going
to go one way or the other."**

*–Jaromir Jagr, on what he does with the loads
of Kit Kat bars that fans send him*

Answers

1. Cleveland Indians
2. New York Mets
3. Pittsburgh Pirates
4. Atlanta Hawks
5. Winnipeg Jets
6. Kansas City Chiefs
7. Montreal Expos
8. Seattle Seahawks
9. Houston Oilers
10. Cincinnati Reds

FULL SEASON

Sec. 17
Row K
Seat 22
Gate F

"Help him up after a play, pat him on the backside, talk to him. Keep him happy. If you get him angry, he's liable to hurt somebody."

–Vikings coach Bud Grant, on Mean Joe Greene